Dear Jo,

Thank you for all your

Raise your vibr

with

THE MIND BODY & SOUL WORKOUT GUIDE

and let your inner light

Shine!

Love
Diana xx

DIANABROOK

natural health & healing

For my boys, Will & Gabe.

Love Mum xx

First published in 2014

Copyright © Diana Brook 2014

Published by Diana Brook.

The information and advice contianed in this book
are intended as a general guide. The author cannot
be held responsible for claims arising from the
inappropriate use of any remedy or exercise regime.
Do not attempt self-diagnosis or self-treatment for
serious or long-term conditions before consulting a
medical professional.

ISBN 978-0-9928990-0-4

RRP - £12.99 (UK)

CONTENTS

Foreword

by Becky Walsh

As a radio presenter on LBC 97.3, I was a spiritual agony aunt of sorts, taking calls from people who felt stuck on a life issue and giving them solutions to their problems. I also interviewed top experts, speakers and authors in the field of self-development: men and women who have brilliant minds insightful on the human condition. In my private practice I act as a shift-catalyst for people who feel like they got stuck on life's rocks, are not in flow and feel unable to achieve their potential. You might say I am a little obsessed with the notion of being stuck!

When you're stuck, you're not really living. Life is too short to not be living it with optimum health, vitality, love, joy and above all balance! Of course the majority of us need to work to live, but it's how we are able to hear ourselves that allows us to choose what is right for who we are and not make limited decisions through fear. 'Stuck' is simply a holding point while you are waiting for more information. Once you have that information you flow free!

Diana Brook has created a relevant book for our time to allow you to live in balance. She has gathered the information required for you to live in optimum health, vitality, and to be able to hear yourself. That's because right now we are presented with more information than ever before. It becomes hard to discern what is right for us personally. It can lead to what psychologists call a state of ambivalence. We become so overwhelmed that we make no decisions at all, i.e. 'stuck'! Diana's book shows you how to hear your body, free your mind and connect fully with your spiritual energy, which is your life's vitality. In doing so you can hear your intuition and know what is right for you. The book is also crammed with useful tips that, if followed, could create dramatic results.

Everyone lives through times when they feel more like they're drowning than in flow - Diana's book is a hand up to find inner stillness in a world of choppy water.

Becky Walsh is...

...one of the world's leading authorities on self-belief and intuition.

She has hosted her own award-winning radio show on LBC 97.3 UK and now presents a show on Hay House radio Spotlight UK. Becky is a Hay House author of 'You DO Know – Learning to Act on Intuition Instantly' as well as three more published books. Becky is often delivering comment and analysis in the media worldwide and is a blogger for the Huffington Post. She regularly travels to address gatherings in places such as Hong Kong, Pakistan, Chile and the USA, and has been a speaker at the 'I Can Do It' Seminar in London. Becky has a live show in which she blends stand-up comedy with live intuition insights on the audience.
Her teaching also effortlessly blends her unique humour with ground-breaking, smack-on-the-forehead insights that put YOU in the driving seat of your life.
www.beckywalsh.com

What people are saying...

"Diana has the utmost integrity and is a born healer, who is excellent at empowering others and encouraging people to think positively. Diana genuinely loves to help others succeed in their lives, body and soul, and I have personally witnessed this on many occasions where she has gone out of her way to help others achieve their chosen paths through self-belief and treating their mind and body well, to ensure a prosperity mind-set." - *Kevin Green, business expert*

"In this book Diana touches on various aspects needed to achieve a balanced and healthy lifestyle. She shares tips, exercises and recipes to help others gain support in taking steps to achieve overall wellbeing." - *Alison Forge, author of Pocket Positivity*

"It is so easy to undermine our health with today's lifestyles. But if you want to find balance and do this in a natural way then this book is for you. Diana's energy, compassion and insights make this book a delight to read and enjoy." - *Niki Schafer, author of Creating Space*

"Diana Brook is an insightful, switched on girl, so no wonder this is such a wise, practical and accessible guide to creating an exciting new you." - *T!M Freke, standup philosopher and international bestselling author*

"The Mind, Body & Soul Workout Guide is sensational. The variety of the course is superb and challenging in the most positive and enlightened way!" - *Lesley Gerrard, MBS client*

"Diana is a fantastic mentor who has guided me every step of the way in my personal journey in creating a healthy relationship with myself and food. Her Workout Guide has inspired me to lead a healthier lifestyle, which has left me bursting and smiling with energy." - *Rachel Jenkins, MBS client*

"Since I've completed the Mind, Body & Soul Workout Guide my whole life has been put back on track, from my perceptions of myself to my own actions, nutrition and exercise. Thank you Diana for helping me take that step in the right direction." - *Philip Perry, MBS client*

Step out of your head, live from the heart!

Improving every aspect of your life in seven simple steps might sound too good to be true, but trust me - it's not!

I have pioneered The Mind, Body & Soul Workout Guide to help bring those three elements into alignment so you can get the most out of your life. But please don't take the name of the book to represent some sort of order of importance; all three work together, support each other and support you, so look after them all equally and you'll feel the benefits!

So, get prepared to learn how to nourish and tune your body, energise your soul with light and vibration, and release your mind from the prison you've built for it, all in the most natural and healthy way possible. You'll love the outcome of a more confident, glamorous you!

Remember, there's no point in a healthy lifestyle if you don't enjoy it!

In this book I want to tell you a little about what I call 'my health philosophy'. That's how I describe a way of taking care of your physical health by taking control of your life - it's partly about how you treat your body but also how you treat your mind.

I think you all understand the impact thought can have on the physical body - it's pretty well established that laughter can indeed be the best medicine as our thoughts create electric responses in our brains, which affect our hormonal body chemistry and therefore every part of us. The most obvious example is stress - so many physical illnesses are symptomatic of stress within our lives, making it obvious how strong the link between body and mind really is.

So, what I want you to think about is how to let go of those stresses and worries and try not to spend too much time self-analysing, reviewing things outside of your control or letting life's unavoidable stresses consume your precious brain-time any more than they absolutely have to.

Let your positive thoughts and feelings blossom, relax into them and let them guide you and the process becomes so much easier. Likewise, looking after your body helps to alleviate stress and strains and helps you to be aware of yourself in the present moment.

And the best part is, it's a self-perpetuating cycle! Free yourself from negative thoughts and you'll feel better in your body and soul. Feel better in your body and soul and your mind will get naturally happier with it, and so on! If you want happiness and prosperity, you will have to put in some work, but trust me - you'll love the results.

Natural health and healing wishes,

So, here's a little bit about me...

Probably much like yourself, I'm a regular working mum and - probably much like yourself - I've had some challenges in my life.

I have found that, sometimes, challenges and hardships are pretty much unavoidable - that's all part of being a human being in the modern world.

I've had to deal with the emotional ups and downs of bouncing back from a divorce and coming to terms with what that meant for my two boys, then walking away from another relationship that came with a millionaire lifestyle - it's certainly been an adventure, and not always an easy one by any stretch of the imagination! There have been moments of great elation and moments of incredible stress.

So the only way to make sure that my circumstances didn't dictate my life was to make sure my life determines my circumstances. Taking charge of my own body and my own mind has given me a sense of direction and peace in my soul, using simple techniques that I've been sharing with others for years in my position as a natural health teacher and practitioner, light therapist and lover of yoga, healthy eating and healthy thinking.

In my face-to-face classes these methods have helped dozens of people to take control of their own lives in a way that lasts. This isn't a fad diet or short-term pick-me-up, this is a way of living that will make you happier and more satisfied in a way that you'll enjoy.

I'm here to share it with you...

How it works

This Workout Guide is easy to follow. Each chapter should take a week of repeated practise (though don't be afraid to read ahead if you like), so that by the end of two months you'll have a completely different outlook on your own life.

To help quantify that, I'd advise that you start by keeping a journal - start before Step 1 by noting down what you want to get out of this Guide, then update it as you go, especially before and after each Workout Excerise - many of which are meditations. You'll really see a change!

Step 1

A NEW PERSPECTIVE

Step 1 **goal**: Know your prosperous self

I want to share with you my holistic knowledge and show you how to apply practical lifestyle patterns to your daily routine in seven easy steps. From my own experience I feel it's better to take small, simple and realistic steps to boost health and vitality - long term.

My approach is simple: clean up toxic thoughts, clean up toxic diet and toxic products, all to raise your aura's energetic vibration. You'll see how it all fits together as we go, and we're going to start with Step 1, your state of mind...

It might sound impossible to reprogramme the way your mind works, but it really isn't, and the first step to doing it is realising why you need to.

It all starts with willingness, commitment and opening yourself up to a new perception. The best chance you have at improving your quality of life is through believing in a better you. You know it's in there - think back to the last time you lost a little weight, for example, or the last time you completed a project you were particularly challenged by, and you'll realise the potential inside you that perhaps you've left dormant for a little too long.

So, what do you need to do?

Step 1 is both the simplest and the most challenging of the whole Mind, Body & Soul Workout Guide - there are no difficult exercises, no time spent in gym-clothes or in the kitchen, no sweat on your brow! But there is a level of admission, acceptance, and above all willingness to raise your consciousness by identifying your fears and the patterns of behaviour that are potentially destructive to the goal of helping you to be who you want to be.

Diana says

"Remember, this all links into the mind-body-soul triumvirate
- you need to work on each to
allow them to support each other."

Get SMART

Let's get down to details. The goal of this step is to help you to start living outside of the limits you impose on yourself, to move out of your own mind and into your heart.

To go about this, I recommend you set clear intentions that fit your lifestyle. They need to work for you and not become too prescriptive. In fact, they should be:

Specific Measurable Achievable Realistic Timely

I know that everyone is different, which means everyone's goal will be different. When you picked up this book, what was it about the text or the images that appealed to you? Do you want to be physically lighter or more flexible, do you want to feel more alert and more present, do you want to enjoy happiness on a more regular basis, do you want to improve your relationships with other people?

What is your new goal for change? Whatever it is, however lofty or simple, now is the time to make a commitment to it - throughout this book I'll be referring a lot to 'prosperity' and this means something different for everyone. Go on, write it down - now is a great time to start making some entries in your journal with your top three goals for changes - it could be your relationships, personal life, health & fitness, having more fun, improving finances, a career-change or something community-based.

Time for a journal entry - note your top 3 goals

A prosperous you

The notion of a prosperous you starts with your state of mind. You've heard people say that it helps to live positively and there's plenty of research to prove it. It's a vital key to the 'mind' part of the mind, body and soul combination.

Let's face it - there are good things in your life and there are probably bad things too. Dwelling on the latter just sets you up for more of the same - a positive mind is more open to opportunities to succeed, more possibilities to be happy and prosperous. A negative mind is just looking for the next negative thing to come along so it can feed off it. There are parts of the world that our outside our control, but what is inside our control is how we react to them.

Part of my teaching is to understand our own mind's propensity to "think in lack," which is to say to always be analysing what we are missing, what we don't have, what we need. It's surprisingly simple to switch this around, and think in terms of what we do have. Gratitude for all that's good in your life brings more peace than, for example, fiscal prosperity, and finding peace with yourself will benefit your mind, your body and your soul.

A prosperity mindset beats a poverty mindset any day of the week, so think prosperous, eat prosperous and live prosperous and you'll feel the advantages. You'll cleanse your aura, free your mind and - with the added benefits of healthy eating - clear out toxic beliefs, toxic diet and toxic vibration.

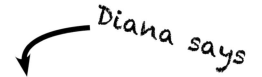

Diana says

"Open up to a new perception. Try to step out of your head and away from the fear that lives there, and instead live from your true self - your heart. This way you will be in alignment and can live your true purpose."

So what's holding you back?

I'll tell you what - it's fear:

 alse

 vidence

In his epic, Dune, the author Frank Herbert wrote: "I must not fear. Fear is the mind-killer. Fear is the little-death that brings total obliteration. I will face my fear. I will permit it to pass over me and through me."

It sounds a little melodramatic but Herbert was right: fear is a weapon that holds us back against ourselves. The first step to overcoming it is understanding that it only exists within our minds. There is nothing tangible to fear; it is an artificial restraint.

Understand that part of your ego, allow yourself to see the truth about how your own unconscious mind controls negative decisions and negative patterns of behaviour. You will realise that the little

A ppearing

voices of doubt chattering inside you are simply figments of an illusory self - a separation from the person you really are. Once you let yourself realise that, you'll be able to surrender it.

Release that old paradigm, fixated on the world around you, and embrace the new that knows your real inner self and understands the value of your inner experiences. The heart, not the head.

R eal

It's the first step toward harmonising the mind, body and soul, and eventually it will lead from being just an inner experience and start to shape your world in real, tangible ways.

This is the heart of the Mind, Body & Soul Workout I teach and it's how you can start to make a difference to the life you're living.

Time for a journal entry - list your top 3 fears

Diana says

"'Laughter is the best medicine', and as science learns more about how the body works the evidence is piling up to prove it - our thoughts shape our bodies in the same way as what we eat or how we live."

Do thoughts really matter?

Cynics could easily ask: "What does it matter? What does how I think about a thing mean to that thing, which is beyond my control?"

Well, the fascinating fact is that how we think is about far more than just an opinion-forming exercise. Believe it or not, our way of thinking has a practical, very real effect on our physical bodies. Epigenetics is the study of how our thought processes have direct impacts on our bodies' genetic make-up, physically altering the way that we are built. There are dozens of genes within humans that are activated by emotional responses triggered by thoughts, and these genes can affect your immune system and your resistance to disease.

Renowned biologist Bruce Lipton states: "I was exhilarated by the new realisation that I could change the character of my life by changing my beliefs. I was instantly energised because I realised that there was a science-based path that would take me from my job as a perennial "victim" to my new position as "co-creator" of my destiny."

"When your ears aren't filled with chatter and the cacophony of negativity," adds Dawson Church PhD, author of The Genie In Your Genes, "and your life is free of stress-generated mindless actions and the prolonged cleanup operations that result from the subsequent mess, then the still, small voice of spirit may be heard… experiments show that measurable molecular changes in the DNA molecule can result from human desires, intentions, and emotions."

So what is the best way to think?

Mindfulness is a word you'll notice me use a lot throughout this guide. For a book that asks you to reflect on your life and make different decisions, you may be a little surprised to hear me say this, but completely clearing your mind - rather than thinking too hard - can often be the best way to progress your life.

Mindfulness has its roots in Buddhist tradition and pertains to a state of being truly here and now. Not thinking of the future, not thinking of the past. It's a surprisingly non-spiritual way of thinking that is fully-grounded in the physical realities of the present, and yet it opens up such doors to spiritual peace that it can really change the way you think and feel.

It is often recommended by mental health experts, such as Andy Puddicombe (mindfulness expert and co-founder of Headspace) who says: "The beautiful thing about mindfulness is that no matter where we go, what we are doing or who we are with, we always have the opportunity to practice."

Opposite is a simple series of practical tips that can help you explore mindfulness for yourself. Use these methods to accept where you are now, without judgement:

MINDFULNESS

1 Close your eyes. Take two deep breaths, focus on your objective to be present. Allow yourself to be curious about it, and let go of any discomfort or fear you may be feeling.

2 Let yourself feel your own body. Concentrate on your own feet on the floor, the feel of whatever your hands are touching, any and all physical sensations you are experiencing. Don't apply any thoughts to them, just feel.

3 This goes for sounds and smells; just let them in and try not to let your mind wander. If it does, if thoughts start to appear, it's no problem - just pull yourself back to that purely physical place. Notice any time a thought appears, gently let go of it, and ignore any distractions that come along. Keep breathing. Don't get frustrated when your mind drifts into thoughts. Keep it effortless and smooth and feel that awareness. When you open your eyes you will feel calmer, more refreshed and more aware.

About meditation

I'm a big fan of mediation because it allows us to tune in to the peace within us and offer awareness in the present moment. The practice of meditation helps to quieten the mind, observe without judgement, and connect to our authentic self.

The best part is that the benefits of meditation are cumulative: it helps to clear the mind, improve concentration, gain clarity by transforming our fear mindset and expand our consciousness.

When we constantly reinforce 'lack' in our thoughts by focussing on fear or loss, we are re-affirming a 'poverty' mindset and consciousness. Inversely, prosperity flows when we think, breathe, talk and act with love and happiness.

To begin your journey within, it is important to be comfortable during your mediation practice. The inhale and exhale of the breath is through the nose, and it helps to keep your spine in an upright position to allow the chakras to align (there will be more on the importance of your amazing chakras later in the guide). Set your intention to be relaxed yet remain with alert attention.

So let's get comfortable and begin with this week's meditation.

Step 1
workout exercise:
Prosperity
meditation

Time for a journal entry — make a note of how you feel before and after meditation

- Sitting comfortably, gently close your eyes
- Bring your awareness to the rhythm of your breath
- On each inhale, draw your awareness inwards, sink deeper into relaxation
- On each exhale, let go of any tension in your physical body
- Release any negativity which you may be experiencing
- Now feel your energy flowing with ease

- Breathing in, silently say to yourself: *"I flow in rhythm with my body, mind and soul"*
- Breathing out silently say to yourself: *"I welcome prosperity into all areas of my life"*
- Breathing in silently say to yourself: *"I flow in rhythm with my body, mind and soul"*
- Breathing out silently say to yourself: *"I welcome prosperity into all areas of my life"*
- Allow yourself to settle with each affirmation and connect with your authentic self
- When you feel ready, gently open your eyes and release the affirmations
- Namaste (bringing your hands together in front of you)

Step 1 affirmation: "I choose not to look back in anger or forward in fear, but around with awareness."

Step 2

NUTRIENTS IN TOXINS OUT

Step 2 **goal**:
Eat real food & use
natural products

In the last century, the rate of diabetes across the globe has increased around 100,000%. As food scientist Jonathon Bailor puts it, "the 'eat less + excercise more = weight loss' equation simply doesn't add up," and the reason for that is sugar.

In this chapter I'm going to expose the myth of fat making you fat, expose the truth that sugar and processed food are your enemy, and I'm going to expose a few of my favourite recipes for simple things to cook at home that will make you feel, and look, better!

Who really needs a sugar rush?

I'm waging a war on sugar. It lowers your energy levels and depletes vitamins and minerals in your body. In the first instance sugar gives you a quick burst of energy which increases blood sugar levels, but then it leaves you feeling tired and hungry fairly quickly when blood sugar levels decrease.

Avoiding this rapid rise or 'spike' and subsequent rapid lowering or 'crash' in your blood sugar level is a fundamental element of this guide. A far better principle to adopt is to balance blood sugar levels by eating nutrient-rich food such as non-starchy vegetables, essential fatty acids, lean protein, nuts and seeds.

Sugar has the same impact on our body as starch, in that they both affect insulin levels. Excess sugar releases large amounts of insulin into the bloodstream, so keeping insulin levels balanced positively impacts the body's ability to burn body fat and maintain energy levels.

For some, when we have an emotional upset or an emotional high we reach for something sugary as a comfort or reward. We associate sugary foods with a range of emotions, and that may become emotionally addictive. Unfortunately, this only triggers a downward spiral.

When you reach for that huge slice of cake drenched in sprinkles, recognise the cake for what it really is: a mass of sugar that leaves your body toxic!

My food philosophy

Abig part of my workout guide is the interaction between mind, body and soul. As will become clear, the three rely upon each other and therefore it's important to look after each independently.

The two most important influences upon your physical body are a) what you put in it and b) what you do with it. We'll cover 'b' in a later chapter, but for now let's focus on 'a', and that means food.

There are some fairly simple rules I tend to live by, that I've used to create the meal planner later in this Step. All those I teach this guide to tell me that their lives really are enriched by following these pearls of wisdom:

Keep blood **sugar** levels balanced

Keep hormones levels **balanced** to regulate fat metabolism system

Eat carbohydrates and protein **together**

Remember that **essential** fatty acids are key to weight management

Eat **antioxidant** superfoods

Include **probiotics** for good digestive health

Sugar cravings can be overcome and you will feel the benefits of reducing your sugar intake. For the next few weeks I highly recommend you avoid white refined sugar and give up alcohol completely, then notice the results and become aware of how you feel.

Something as simple as reducing the amount of sugar you have in a hot drink, or not using sugar as a reward is a good way to start making a positive change.

Speaking from experience, when I started cutting back on sugar my taste buds changed. Yours will too! You'll be amazed at how quickly you will adapt and become more sensitive to the taste of sugar in foods.

7 ways to eat, and live, healthily

1
Nutrients in
Eat fresh food as close to its natural state as possible:

Fresh food is rich in nutrients; vitamins, minerals, amino acids and essential fatty acids provide quality calories which are important in the release of fat burning hormones.

2
Toxins out
Eliminate processed foods:

Processed food is packed with artificial additives, saturated fat, sugar and salt. In other words, it's full of harmful toxins that you want to avoid during your cleansing programme.

5
Make your skin glow
Your skin is the largest organ of your entire body:

It's important to take care of your skin. Use a firm natural bristle brush for daily skin brushing prior to your shower in the morning, to clear dead skin cells and debris. This will allow your skin to breathe, stimulate circulation and support lymph drainage.

6
Be conscious
Take time to savour food:

Simply be in the present moment to enjoy every mouthful, use your senses to taste every bite, take time to chew your food and be mindful of what your body is telling you to avoid over-eating or filling an emotional hunger.

3
It's all about balance
Eat seasonal fruits and vegetables and balance with protein:

Fill up on a naturally balanced plate will keep hormone and blood sugar levels balanced, which will help burn fat and reduce fat-storing hormones.

4
Hydrate your body
Create a hydration habit:

Start your day with a cup of hot water and a fresh slice of lemon. This is great way to kickstart your digestive system. Aim to drink water regularly throughout the day to help prevent constipation and reduce bloating.

7
Change your perception
Avoid weighing yourself regularly; this way you cut down toxic thoughts:

The number on the scale will not tell you how your body feels, how much energy you have, how well you slept and will definitely not define what a unique person you are!

Plus! For more pearls of wisdom and regular updates, keep up with my blog: www.dianabrook.co.uk

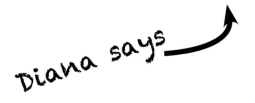
Diana says

The truth about fatty acids

When it comes to food and nutrition, one of the biggest misconceptions going is that fat makes you fat.

Society is obsessed with low-fat and fat-free products, thinking they are healthier, but this simply is not true. In fact, the majority of foods that are labelled low-fat or fat-free are refined, highly processed foods where the fat has simply been replaced with more sugar to maintain flavour. Not a good option!

The truth is that many fats are very healthy, essential to our wellbeing, and even promote weight loss. After all, our body requires fat in order to function properly.

Many entirely necessary vitamins, such as A, D, E, and K are fat-soluble, meaning the only way your body can absorb them is in the presence of fat. On the next few pages I'll show you a few types of good fats (essential fatty acids) that are great to incorporate into your nutrition. Not only will you feel better, but your body won't feel deprived or hungry!

Diana says

"The best form of sugar is low-fructose fruit like blueberries, raspberries, blackberries, melon and kiwi. I always eat with handful of nuts to slow down the rate that sugar enters the bloodstream."

My top five fatty foods that are actually GREAT for you

1- Avocados

I absolutely love avocados. And it's not just because they taste great and are incredibly versatile - they are also an excellent source of glutathione, which is a powerful antioxidant that helps cleanse and protect your body by detoxifying, removing heavy metals, and fighting free radicals. Glutathione also helps maintain a healthy immune system and slows the aging process. Pretty amazing, huh?

Avocados are rich in folate, which has been shown to decrease the incidence of heart disease and stroke, and they are also the best fruit source of vitamin E, which is a powerful antioxidant and the ultimate vitamin for skin food - essential for DNA repair. So stop reading this and go add avocados to your shopping list!

2 - Nuts

Nuts are my go-to snack, loaded with amazing nutrients, healthy fats, and protein.

They are the best source of alpha-linolenic acid or omega-3, which offers numerous health benefits including lowering cholesterol and aiding metabolism. Packed with protein, nuts are rich in L-arginine, an essential amino acid that is one of the building blocks of proteins in the body and has been shown to boost immune function, promote improve blood vessel function, and help manage cardiovascular disease.

They're a great source of vitamin E, a powerful antioxidant essential for proper immune function and healthy skin.

4 - Olive oil

I only ever cook with olive oil at moderate temperatures as the chemical structure changes, becomng unstable at high temperatures. I love to use it as a dipping oil or pouring over salads. It is rich in monounsaturated fat and antioxidants such as chlorophyll, carotenoids and vitamin E.

It is great for reducing blood pressure, reducing cancer risk, and managing diabetes and the severity of asthma and arthritis. And it tastes delicious!

3 - Seeds

Seeds are so versatile - as a snack or simply sprinkled on your breakfast or salads. Plus they're packed with health-promoting minerals like magnesium, selenium and zinc. And they are a rich source of fibre, omega-3 fatty acids and protein - I'd recommend flax, pumpkin, sunflower and chia.

Chia seeds in particular are considered a superfood due to their extremely high nutrient profile. Super rich in omega-3s, they are loaded with powerful antioxidants, phosphorous, manganese, copper and iron.

5 - Coconut

Coconut is delicious and so versatile. I love to add coconut water to smootheis, coconut milk to curries and rice. Coconut oil is excellent for cooking at high temperatures, and it has anti-fungal, anti-inflammatory and anti-cancer properties. Plus it improves digestion, nutrient absorption and intestinal health.

The benefits don't stop there - coconut oil promotes kidney and liver health and supports the immune system. It also benefits metabolism and weight management.

It's not just for the kitchen - it's fantastic to use on your skin too!

Your 7-day plan

	MONDAY	TUESDAY	WEDNESDAY
BREAKFAST	Crunchy Homemade Granola	Fruity Porridge	Perfect Poached Eggs & Avocado on Spelt Bread
LUNCH	Open Chicken Salad Sandwich	Grilled Vegetables & Goats Cheese Salad	Quinoa, Butternut Squash & Black-bean Cakes
SNACK	Brilliant Balancing Smoothie	Probiotic Yoghurt with Granola Topping	Oatcakes with Hummus & Sundried Tomatoes
DINNER	Creamy Risotto with Greens	Sizzling Steak with Sweet Potato Wedges	Fresh Fish Kebabs with Salsa

for healthy living

THURSDAY	FRIDAY	SATURDAY	SUNDAY
Signature Kickstart Green Smoothie	Probiotic Yoghurt with Nuts & Seeds	Blueberry Buckwheat Pancake Stack	2 Egg Omlette
Tasty Tuna Pittas	Comforting Beetroot & Feta Salad	Simply Sweet Potato Soup	Super-Speedy Stir Fry
Oaty & Nutty Energy Bars	Gooey Gucamole on Spelt Bread	Blistering Berry Smoothie	Chia & Oat Smoothie
Tantalising Thai Vegetable Curry	Green Pesto-Topped Salmon	Rice Noodles with Prawns	Sweet Potato Mash with Coconut Chicken

Breakfast

whatever you do, don't skip it!

Crunchy homemade granola

YOU WILL NEED...

175g organic jumbo porridge oats
75g buckwheat flakes
75g raisins
75g cranberries
75g coconut flakes

75g sunflower seeds
75g pumpkin seeds
75g flaked almonds
75g chopped walnuts
Natural yoghurt to serve

HERE'S HOW IT'S DONE...

Combine all dry ingredients and spoon approximately 3 heaped dessertspoons per person into bowls.

Top with natural yoghurt.
Store any remaining oat mixture in a covered container in a cool, dark place for up to 2 weeks.

Serves 8
This is an excellent source of magnesium which helps to keep the heart healthy. Also, it contains zinc which is important for a healthy immune system, and iron, needed for healthy red blood cells.

Fruity porridge

YOU WILL NEED...

175g porridge oats
250ml rice, sesame, almond or
goat's milk

250ml water
Flaked almonds
Handful of fresh or dried berries

HERE'S HOW IT'S DONE...

Mix the oats, milk and water in a
saucepan.

Stir and bring to the boil, heating
through until thickened.

Serve with honey (optional) and sprinkle
flaked almonds and fruit of your choice.

Serves 4

Perfect poached eggs with avocado on spelt bread

YOU WILL NEED...

2tsp cider vinegar
4 fresh large free range eggs
4 medium slices spelt bread

4 baby plum tomatoes
Freshly ground black pepper

HERE'S HOW IT'S DONE...

Bring a saucepan of water to the boil, add the vinegar. Once boiling, break the eggs into a cup and slip into the water, spacing well apart and reduce the heat to low.

Cook the eggs gently for approximately 3-4 minutes for a softer set yolk.

Meanwhile, toast the bread and slice avocado.

Drain the eggs with slotted spoon and layer on the toast with avocado and eggs. Garnish with baby plum tomatoes.

Serves 4

Signature kickstart green smoothie

YOU WILL NEED...

3-4 handfuls of baby spinach leaves
1 large stalk of kale (leaves only)
1 small banana
A few chunks of pineapple
8fl oz coconut water

Juice of half a lemon
1 dessert spoon of beauty oil (available from www.dianabrook.co.uk/Shop.aspx)
1 tsp spirulina

HERE'S HOW IT'S DONE...

Wash and prep all the ingredients, chopping the banana and pineapple into chunks. Place all the ingredients into a blender and whizz until smooth, topping up with more coconut water if needed.

Serve immediately.
Serves 2
Feel free to substitute fruit with mango, pear or kiwi.

Blueberry buckwheat pancake stack

YOU WILL NEED...

300ml almond, coconut or goat's milk
250g buckwheat flour
175g blueberries

4 eggs
2 tbsp of coconut oil
Natural yoghurt (optional)

HERE'S HOW IT'S DONE...

Whisk the milk and egg together in a large bowl, then gradually add buckwheat flour. Whisk well until you have a smooth, creamy batter. Stir in the blueberries (optional). Heat oil in a frying pan, spoon in a ladle of the batter.

After 2-3 minutes, flip and cook on the other side and repeat.

Layer the pancakes and blueberries and serve with a spoonful of natural yoghurt.
Serves 1

Probiotic yoghurt with nuts & seeds

YOU WILL NEED...

300ml live probiotic yoghurt
1 dessert spoon of mixed nuts of your choice (I personally love a mixture of pistachios & almonds)

1 dessert spoon of pumpkin seeds
1 tsp ground linseed
Drizzle of honey (optional)

HERE'S HOW IT'S DONE...

Spoon the yoghurt into a bowl, sprinkle a layer of mixed nuts, pumpkin seeds and, finally, sprinkle over ground linseeds. You can add a drizzle of honey, but not too much!

Serves 1 as a quick and easy breakfast for when you are on the go!

2 egg omlette

YOU WILL NEED...

2 eggs
A pinch of sea salt
A pinch of black pepper
1 tsp sunflower oil
Herbs of your choice

Filling options:
Turkey, mushrooms & spring onions
Red pepper, ham & red onion
Smoked salmon & watercress
Tomato, spinach, mushrooms & basil

HERE'S HOW IT'S DONE...

Crack the eggs into a bowl and beat with a fork until smooth. Season the eggs with salt and pepper and stir in herbs of your choice. Heat sunflower oil in a non-stick frying pan; add your chosen ingredients to the pan. Add the egg mixture. Cook until golden underneath, but slightly soft and clear on the top. Flip the omelette over and cook for another minute. To serve fold the omelette in half and enjoy.

Serves 1

Lunch

it's worth a little bit of prep

Quinoa, butternut squash and blackbean cakes

YOU WILL NEED...

1 medium butternut squash (cubed)
90g black beans (soaked)
60g quinoa (cooked)
2 tbsp coconut oil

1 garlic clove, crushed
1 red chilli (optional)
Handful of coriander, roughly chopped
Freshly ground pepper

HERE'S HOW IT'S DONE...

Preheat oven to 190C. Roast the butternut squash with garlic for 30 mins until soft.

Place cooked squash in a large bowl and mix in quinoa, black beans and chopped coriander, adding the chilli if desired. Season to taste.

Refridgerate for 30 mins, then mould into cakes.

Heat the coconut oil in a pan, then fry for 2 ½ mins each side.

Serves 4-6 with a green salad

This recipe can be prepared the night before, it's a great alternative to sandwiches in your lunch box, and can be eaten hot or cold.

Simply sweet potato soup

YOU WILL NEED...

1 onion
3 sticks of celery
2 diced carrots
1 chopped yellow pepper
1 tbsp olive oil

900ml vegetable stock
Salt and pepper
4 diced sweet potatoes
1 can (400ml) of coconut milk
Chopped coriander

HERE'S HOW IT'S DONE...

Chop the onion, dice the celery, carrots and pepper and place in a large saucepan with the olive oil and sweat vegetables for approx 5-10 mins.

Add the vegetable stock, sweet potatoes and bring to the boil, simmer for 15mins

until the sweet potatoes are tender. Add the coconut milk and season with salt and pepper. Liquidise in a blender then add chopped coriander.

Serves 4

Super-speedy stir fry

YOU WILL NEED...

1 tbsp coconut oil
1 clove garlic, chopped
1 chilli, chopped, deseeded
1 onion, chopped
100g beef breast, sliced (optional)

Handful of asparagus
Handful of broccoli
Handful of mangetout
Soy sauce (gluten free optional)
Handful of coriander, chopped

HERE'S HOW IT'S DONE...

Heat the oil in a wok or frying pan until hot.

Add the garlic, chilli and onion and fry for 1 min.

Add the beef and cook for approx 3 mins, until almost cooked through. Add the vegetables and cook for a couple of mins, add the soy sauce and stir in the coriander.

Serves 1 with rice noodles (optional)

Open chicken salad sandwich

YOU WILL NEED...

Sliced cooked chicken
½ avocado
½ yellow pepper
3-4 leaves baby gem lettuce
2-4 sundried tomatoes
1 dessert spoon of pesto
1 slice spelt bread

HERE'S HOW IT'S DONE...

Spread pesto on spelt bread, then layer
with baby gem lettuce, sliced avocado,
yellow pepper and slices of chicken. Top
with sundried tomatoes.
Serves 1

Grilled vegetables with goat's cheese & rice salad

YOU WILL NEED...

100g brown rice
2tsp olive oil
1 red & yellow pepper, diced
1 medium leek, trimmed and sliced
150g green beans, trimmed
1 head broccoli, cut into small florets
125g frozen peas
8oz soft mild goat's cheese

HERE'S HOW IT'S DONE...

Cook rice according to packet. While the
rice is cooking, heat oil in a large frying
pan and cook the pepper and leek for 5
mins until soft and very lightly browned,
stirring regularly. Set aside to cool.
Bring a medium pan of water to the boil,
add the beans and cook for 2 mins, then
add the broccoli and peas. Return water
to the boil, then drain in a colander.
Toss all the vegetables with the cooked
rice and season with ground black
pepper. Spoon onto plates and top with
crumbled goat's cheese.
Serves 4 with a large mixed salad

Comforting beetroot, butternut squash & feta salad

YOU WILL NEED...

3 tbsp olive oil
2 level tsp clear honey
500g butternut squash, peeled & sliced
1 red onion, sliced into rounds
300g cooked beetroot, sliced
150g steamed tenderstem broccoli
50g walnut halves
1 tbsp red wine vinegar
½ tsp Dijon mustard
70g rocket or leaves of your choice
100g feta cheese, broken into pieces

HERE'S HOW IT'S DONE...

Preheat oven to 170C. Line two baking trays
with baking paper. Put 1tbsp of the oil and
1tsp of the honey in a bowl and season.
Whisk the oil and honey to combine,
add the butternut squash and onion. Toss
together, coat well and place on baking tray.
Bake for 15 minutes.
Add the beetroot to the baking tray and
return to the oven for another 15 minutes.
Leave to cool, as you place walnut halves
on the baking tray and cook in the oven for
5 minutes.
Whisk the rest of the oil with the vinegar,
mustard and 1tsp honey, then toss with
cooled cooked vegetables.
Place rocket (or leaves) on plate, with
cooked vegetables, walnuts and feta.
Serves 4

Tasty tuna pittas

YOU WILL NEED...

1 small can sweetcorn, drained
1 can tuna in spring water, drained
2 tomatoes, roughly chopped
2 little gem lettuces, trimmed and sliced
1 small red onion, finely sliced
1 garlic clove, peeled and crushed
1 tbsp extra virgin olive oil
3 tbsp chopped fresh parsley
1 lemon, freshly squeezed
4 wholemeal pitta bread, warmed

HERE'S HOW IT'S DONE...

Tip sweetcorn into a large serving
bowl, add the tuna, tomatoes, little
gem lettuce, red onion, garlic, parsley
and lemon juice. Toss together lightly
and season to taste with ground black
pepper. Split the pitta breads and fill
with the tuna mixture.
Serves 4 with fresh green leaves

Snacks

because no-one likes going hungry!

Chia and oat smoothie

YOU WILL NEED...

300mls coconut milk
25g rolled oats
1 small banana
1 tbsp natural yoghurt
1 dessert spoon chia seeds

½ tsp maca powder
Handful of almonds
Handful of sunflower and pumpkin
seeds, plus a little extra for sprinkling
Ice (optional)

HERE'S HOW IT'S DONE...

Place all the ingredients in a blender, whizz until smooth.

Add ice for a thicker consistency - I love my smoothies thick enough to eat with a spoon! Sprinkle sunflower and pumpkin seeds, and enjoy.

Serves 2
Almonds provide a great source of vitamin E, chia provides omega 3 while maca is rich in B vitamins and has plenty of calcium, iron and magnesium.

57

Oaty & nutty energy bars

YOU WILL NEED...

150g porridge oats
75g buckwheat flakes
4 tbsp manuka honey
50g chopped walnuts
50g chopped mixed nuts

25g sunflower seeds
25g pumpkin seeds
25g cranberries
25g desiccated coconut (optional)
1 egg

HERE'S HOW IT'S DONE...

Preheat oven to 200C and lightly grease an 8 inch square, non-stick baking tin.

Combine all ingredients in large bowl and mix together. Press the mixture into the prepared tin.

Bake for 15 mins until golden, then cut into 8 bars, cool and serve.

Makes 8 bars

Blistering berry smoothie

YOU WILL NEED...

2 tsp ground almonds
Handful of blueberries, strawberries,
raspberries and goji berries

2 tbsp natural yoghurt
4fl oz coconut water

HERE'S HOW IT'S DONE...

Wash berries, add all ingredients into
blender, whizz until smooth.

Serve immediately.
Serves 2

Brilliant balancing smoothie

YOU WILL NEED...

200mls of rice, almond or goat's milk
200mls of water
8 tablespoons oats
8 brazil nuts
8 almonds
8 walnuts
4 tsp ground flaxseeds
4 tsp pumpkin seeds
4 tsp chia seeds

HERE'S HOW IT'S DONE...

Place all the ingredients in large glass
and whizz in a blender until smooth.
Drink immediately to maximise all the
balanced nutrients.
Serves 2

Probiotic yoghurt with granola topping

YOU WILL NEED...

175g organic jumbo porridge oats
75g buckwheat flakes
75g raisins
75g cranberries
75g coconut flakes
75g sunflower seeds
75g pumpkin seeds
75g flaked almonds
75g chopped walnuts
Probiotic yoghurt

HERE'S HOW IT'S DONE...

Mix the dry ingredients.

Put the yoghurt in a bowl and top with
the three spoonfuls of the granola. How
easy was that?!
Serves 1

Oatcakes with hummus and sundried tomatoes

YOU WILL NEED...

200g tinned chickpeas
2 tbsp lemon juice
2 cloves garlic, crushed
1 tsp ground cumin
Salt to taste
4 tbsp water
1 tsp paprika
8 oatcakes
Sundried tomatoes

HERE'S HOW IT'S DONE...

To make the hummus, place the chickpeas, lemon juice, garlic, cumin, salt and water in a food processor, and blend until smooth.

Serve on top of oatcakes and sprinkle with finely-chopped sundried tomatoes.
Serves 4

Gooey guacamole on spelt bread

YOU WILL NEED...

1 slice of spelt bread
1 avocado
1 red pepper, chopped
1/2 red chilli, finely sliced (optional)

HERE'S HOW IT'S DONE...

Toast the spelt bread.
While it cooks, skin the avocado and separate the stone from the flesh.
Mash the avocado with a fork and add the red pepper and chilli if desired.
Season to taste and spread on the toast.
Serves 1

Dinner

time to show off in the kitchen!

Tantalising Thai vegetable curry

YOU WILL NEED...

2 tbsp medium Thai curry paste
1 large onion, chopped
1 tsp cumin seeds
2 sweet potatoes
2 carrots
4 baby corn, diced

1 head of broccoli, cut into small florets
1 red pepper, chopped
200ml vegetable stock
150g green beans, trimmed
Brown rice or quinoa to serve

HERE'S HOW IT'S DONE...

Cook the curry paste and onion together in a large pan for 2-3 mins until soft.

Add the cumin seeds, sweet potatoes, carrots, red pepper and broccoli and cook for another 2 mins.

Add the stock, bring to simmer then cover and cook for 15 mins.

Cut the beans and corn in half, add to the pan and cook for a further 10 minutes until all the vegetables are tender. Serve with brown rice or quinoa.

Serves 4
Quinoa has a low GI so keeps you feeling fuller for longer. Also a good source of protein, magnesium, zinc, fibre & vitamin E.

Sweet potato mash with coconut chicken

YOU WILL NEED...

4 chicken breasts, skinned
4 diced sweet potatoes
400ml coconut milk
4-6 baby plum tomatoes
1 dessert spoon red thai curry paste
(optional)

Salt and pepper to season

For the marinade:
3 tbsp olive oil
1 stalk lemongrass, sliced
1 tsp ginger, chopped

HERE'S HOW IT'S DONE...

In a shallow dish mix all the ingredients for the marinade and coat the chicken. Cover in cling film and refrigerate for 30 mins.

Preheat the oven to 180C. Roast the sweet potatoes, skins on or off, for 45 mins.

Roast the marinated chicken for 20 mins, and meanwhile heat the coconut milk and curry paste together, then add baby plum tomatoes and cook until the tomatoes are soft.

Mash the sweet potatoes with salt and pepper, then slice and layer chicken over potato and drizzle on the coconut milk.
Serves 4

Green pesto-topped salmon

YOU WILL NEED...

2 salmon fillets, skinned
50g pine nuts
Large bunch of basil
50g parmesan (or vegetarian alternative)

150ml olive oil, plus extra for storing
2 garlic cloves
Salt and pepper
1 lemon

HERE'S HOW IT'S DONE...

Make the pesto by toasting the nuts in a dry pan then adding to a blender with the basil, cheese, garlic and olive oil. The sauce will keep for up to two weeks in a jar topped with the extra oil.

Brush a non-stick frying pan or griddle with a little oil, heat then add the salmon.

Cook over a moderate heat for 5 mins on each side, covering with a lid. Top each salmon portion with the pesto mixture.

Serve with large salad or seasonal vegetables.

Serves 2

Creamy risotto with greens

Sizzling steak with sweet potato wedges

YOU WILL NEED...

1 tbsp olive oil
1 onion, chopped
150g Arborio (risotto) rice
500ml vegetable stock
200g spinach
125g asparagus
60g peas, fresh or frozen
Zest of 1 lemon (unwaxed)
Handful fresh torn basil leaves
Salt and pepper

HERE'S HOW IT'S DONE...

Heat the oil in a large pan. Add the onion and cook for 2 mins. Add the rice and stir with a wooden spoon until the grains are coated with the oil. Stir in vegetable stock one ladle at a time and simmer for about 10 mins. Add the asparagus, peas, spinach and lemon zest.

Continue cooking for a further 10 mins until all the liquid has been absorbed and the rice is tender but firm in the centre. Stir in the basil leaves and season to taste. Serve immediately.
Serves 2

YOU WILL NEED...

4 sirloin steaks
3 tbsp olive oil
2 large handfuls of spinach
6 sweet potatoes (cut into wedges)
3 tbsp soy sauce

HERE'S HOW IT'S DONE...

Preheat oven to 190C. Cut sweet potatoes into wedges leaving the skins on. Cook for 45 mins, turning occasionally. Take the steaks out of the fridge and allow them to get to room temperature. Approximately 10 mins before the sweet potatoes are ready, heat the frying pan, oil the steaks and cook to your taste, drizzle the soy sauce over the steaks in the pan. Serve immediately with the sweet potatoes and a handful of spinach.

Serves 4

Rice noodles with prawns

YOU WILL NEED...

600g raw prawns
150g tenderstem broccoli
150g mangetout, finely sliced
2 large pak choi
2 tbsp coconut oil
250g rice noodles
1 tsp peeled and grated ginger
1 chilli, sliced (optional)

HERE'S HOW IT'S DONE...

Rinse the prawns under cold water.
Heat the coconut oil in a wok and gently
fry ginger and chilli until soft.
Add the prawns and continue to cook
until pink then add the vegetables.
Meanwhile, cook the rice noodles
according to packet instructions. Serve
the prawns over the noodles and garnish
with chilli.
Serves 2

Fresh fish kebabs

YOU WILL NEED...

4 tbsp olive oil
1 tbsp cider vinegar
1 tsp clear honey
1 tomato
2 spring onions, trimmed and sliced
1 tbsp parsley, chopped
250g cod loin or monkfish, cut into
bitesize chunks
250g salmon fillets, skinned and cut into
bitesize chunks
200g raw king prawns

HERE'S HOW IT'S DONE...

Whisk the oil, cider vinegar and honey
to make a dressing, season to taste.
Quarter the tomato and discard the
seeds. Dice the flesh and stir into the
dressing with the spring onion and
parsley, set aside.
Thread the fish onto skewers and brush
with a little oil. Grill on a medium heat
for 5-10 mins, turning occasionally until
the cod and salmon flake easily and the
prawns turn pink. Drizzle the dressing
over the fish kebabs. Serve with a large
green salad.

So, the nutrients are in, now let's get those toxins out

When you're trying to be healthy, it's easy to focus on the obvious pairing: nutrition and exercise.

When it comes to eating, it's very easy to forget that it's not just our stomachs that absorb nutrients, but also our skin.

Your skin is the largest organ of your whole body, but do you really give much thought to what it's absorbing? Some things, like exhaust fumes and city-smog, can be difficult to avoid, but when it comes to cosmetics, perfumes, lotions and deodorants there is definitely a reason to watch what your skin is eating!

As well as food, let's look a little at the kind of chemicals that your body can absorb, and definitely shouldn't. My tip: read the label.

So let's look at some examples of what NOT to use on your skin, and why:

Parabens

These are synthetic preservatives that are known to be skin irritants. They can cause hormonal disruption by mimicking oestrogen, and are a suspected carcinogen (linked to breast cancer). As they are fat soluble they can enter the fatty tissue of the breast - clearly not a good thing!

Look out for: methylparaben, ethylparaben, butylparaben and propylparaben.

Instead choose: tocopherol, vitamin E, antioxidants and essential oils.

Synthetic fragrances

These are toxic cocktails of chemicals designed to simulate natural smells, and they're simply no good. Derived from petrochemicals (see opposite) these artificial substances are skin irritants and can increase the body's toxic load.

Look out for: 'parfum'.

Instead choose: essential oils.

Petrochemicals

Derived from crude oil, these are unsustainable skin irritants that damage the environment and your skin.

Look out for: parabens, petrolatum, propylene glycol, sodium laureth sulfate or paraffinium.

Instead choose: brazil, hemp, flax seed or wheatgerm oils, and coco glucoside.

Also

Good words to seek out on packaging include 'wild', 'organic', 'natural' and 'Soil Association Certified'.

Diana says

"I always recommend Neal's Yard skincare products – you simply can't go wrong
www.dianabrook.co.uk/shop.aspx"

Step 2

workout exercise:

Get **organised**

1 take **stock** of what's in your **kitchen** and bathroom cupboards

It might seem a little wasteful, but now is the time to bin those chocolate bars, ready meals and toxic products. It takes time but do read the ingredients labels and look for hidden sugars - the most healthy foods provided by nature don't even need ingredients lists!

And remember: if they're not in the house, you won't be tempted.

2 get **organised** with your **nutrition**-packed shopping list

When it comes to being healthy, home cooking is pretty much vital. And home cooking only really happens when you're organised enough to make it happen!

What seems like a chore at first will become second nature soon enough; your cupboards, and your body, will thank you!

Time for a journal entry - how much have you cleared out, and how much better do you feel for it?

3 find your local **health** food shop

Some of the ingredients I've used in these recipes might seem a little obscure, but supermarkets these days are much more obliging than they used to be.

Regardless, there will be times when you'll need a specialist, so check out your Yellow Pages or find a retailer online.

4 during the course keep a **food journal**

This is the meat of your Step 2 Workout Exercise. For the next six weeks - until the end of this course - I want you to keep a food journal as a part of the regular journal you're keeping of your progress. Please, be honest with yourself: that biscuit with your cuppa DOES have to be recorded in the journal, I'm afraid.

When you look back on your journal in a few weeks' time, I'm hopeful you'll see a real change in how you treat your body.

Step 2 affirmation: "I nourish my mind, body and soul and nurture my healthy relationship with food."

Step 3

MEET
YOUR
TRUE SELF

Step 3 **goal**: Have a great relationship with yourself

What are we? It's a question that has confounded philosophers, theologians and scientists since humans first achieved sentiency, and yet these days there is a prevailing answer that seems to me the most rounded - we are what we believe ourselves to be.

That is to say, we are our physical form, we are our mental construct, and we are the spirit that binds it all together - we can sense all three, so why not accept them and live in harmony?

This third step is all about achieving that harmony through calming of the mind; by understanding the voice in our heads and learning to tame it and direct it in a manner that suits our lives and the way we want ourselves to be.

Our mind is a beautiful, marvellous, incredible machine that lets us live and build relationships and be driven to follow our goals, but it can also be a prison; a prison of doubts and distractions and fears that will hold us back if we let them.

Look after it, and it will keep you emotionally stable. Let it rule you, and you will lose sight of the present - mindfulness - and that makes following this prosperity guide much more difficult.

Where am I right now?

Mindfulness - there's that word again. The very best way to get a real grip of your own life is to know where you are, right now. Not on a philosophical or emotional level, but on a completely pragmatic, physical level.

The act of mindfulness is in focusing on the body, but the result of mindfulness is quieting the mind.

We rely on our mind to be focused, creative, spontaneous and to perform at our best, but we need to be able to release the ego's false projection we've created, lest we become slaves to our own mental processes. As we attempt to attain mindfulness and find our bodies, our minds will distract us and pull us away, but we must not be deterred - these skills take practise but the results are well worth it!

We so rarely live in the present moment, savour it, and yet it is such a wonderful place to be.

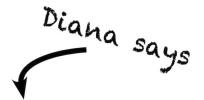

Diana says

"It's so rewarding to know that you can truly master the fear voice in your head!"

Hearing voices?

There's no shame in admitting it - you hear voices in your head. Specifically, your own.

Don't panic! There's nothing more normal in the world than hearing your own brain express itself in your native language. We all do it, and these monologues can prove useful ways of analysing the vast quantities of data that our brains have to intake every day.

But, as when you're trying to concentrate on a difficult task, chatter can be a distraction. In fact, when you think about the amount of chatter one's own mind generates, it's a wonder any of us ever get anything done!

It might seem natural to think that the voice in your head is 100% you, but that's not entirely correct. As I explained at the beginning of this chapter, there's more to you than just your mind, even though your mind certainly likes to adopt a dominant position. If you can keep this chatter in check, you'll be able to better appreciate the value of your body and soul, which is after all why you're reading this guide!

Time for a journal entry - what chatter distracts you day-to-day?

DIANABROOK

See the pattern, take action

Unfortunately, the voice inside your head isn't always the most encouraging. It's a hard fact that it often reminds you of your limitations, or of restrictions you should abide by, or of the dangers of your actions. That's a great natural defence mechanism that no-one could live without, but using fear as your default position is no way to get on and live the life you want.

In the hardest emotional times of my life, I've given in to that fear voice and it's been so hard to claw myself away from it. If we let ourselves keep following the storyline trailed out by our natural internal monologue, we hamper our chances of achievement, and that's a real shame. The trick, which sounds simple but takes a lot of practise and dedication, is to notice when the fear voice is speaking.

So let's observe the patterns of our mind and we'll start to see the patterns of our behaviour. It could be something as simple as trudging through your day-job because your mind is expecting you not to engage and get ahead. It could be down to the fact that your mind is telling you that after dinner you'll have a chocolate bar from the cupboard, or it could be infinitely more complicated than that - I've helped people to hear this voice in dozens of circumstances and they're always different.

The key is that once you start to see the patterns, once you start to understand them, you can start to let them go. And the sense of freedom that brings can be almost overwhelmingly positive!

Diana says

"Taking time to connect with nature gives me the opportunity to objectively observe where I am."

The complex mind/body relationship

Don't get me wrong - this chapter is nothing to do with stopping your mind's thoughts or banishing emotions. There's no benefit from being devoid of such wonders, but understanding them leads to a greater level of control over your life.

Allow yourself to step back, to witness and observe the way your mind works without judgement but with a relaxed focused mind. You'll find it so revealing!

Your natural habit might be to understand yourself as something somehow remote and abstract from your body and mind, or it might be to think of yourself as your mind interacting with your body and soul.

The beautiful fact is that both of these positions are accurate, it's just about finding the right balance between the ego and the whole you - one cannot exist without the other.

Diana says

"As with so much of this guide, understanding is your launch pad. Learn the true essence of your whole self and you'll find it so much easier to really love yourself."

Here's a big question...
what is your soul?

The third part of the mind-body-soul triumvirate is, naturally, the hardest to pin down. Intangible as a concept and yet universally understood across cultures and generations, the soul is really what you choose to make of it.

Your soul, I believe, is the true complete essence of you, and it is light and love. It's the warmth and positivity that make you value all that life has to offer, and it's fostered by the notion that you are not your mind and you are not your body.

In Cave In The Snow, Vicki MacKenzie highlights this point: "Normally we are so identified with our thoughts and emotions, that we are them. We are the happiness, we are the anger, we are the fear. We have to learn to step back and know our thoughts and emotions are just thoughts and emotions. They're just mental states. They're not solid, they're transparent."

What are you worth?

Only you have the answer to this question. You can probably think of dozens of ways of describing yourself, but I'll bet that if you really look at these descriptions - your self image, self confidence, self esteem - you'll realise that this is probably your ego's fear-based description!

So, it's time to cleanse those thoughts and wash away the layers of fear. You really are a wonderful and unique being, we all are, and you deserve your own love. Feed yourself with loving thoughts every single day to help change your mind and shift your perspective. That's the key to becoming the prosperous person you want to be.

To help you work toward the ultimate relationship - self love - here is Robert Holden's version of Love's Prayer:

Time for a journal entry - what do the words 'self love' mean to you?

Beloved One,
You cannot judge yourself and know who you are.
The truth about you cannot be judged,
Put aside your judgements then,
For one sweet holy moment
& let me show you
Something wonderful.

See what it is like to be You
When you stop judging yourself
What you judge is just an image.
After the last judgement,
You will know yourself again.
Love will appear in your own mirror.
To greet you as your friend.
For you are loveable.
& you are made of love.

Reflect and love

Much like we did in Step 1, we're going to meditate as the exercise for Step 3. Whereas in Step 1 we were attempting to step you out of your head and into your heart, we're going to dig a little deeper here, analysing ourselves from a remote position, free of judgement, full of love and understanding.

I have long been a great advocate of meditation, which offers us the opportunity to step back and presents a loving perspective that can let us change our own experience for the better. It's no wonder meditation has been practiced across the ages and across cultures - it simply works!

In this third step I would like you to aim for a greater sense of focus, calm and clarity in your life, using meditation as a technique for a healthy mind and great relationship with yourself. Familiarise yourself with the present moment and keep up your meditation exercises even when you're not feeling on top form - it's an exercise framework that can be used as a preventative measure.

Getting more from meditation

Remember those self-worth questions I presented earlier in this chapter? I want you to ask yourself those questions after you've finished this meditation exercise and notice the difference in your answers - be sure to put them down in your journal.

It takes practise, but try to notice the balance between where you placed your attention and intention between your ego self and authentic self.

To open up to inner peace, health and wellbeing it's important to let go of our monologue, which is always centred around the past or future. Instead we need to enter into dialogue where we experience the NOW.

Being mindful of the present moment transforms those thoughts of suffering that are occupying us. Being in dialogue reminds you that you are greater than your fears, anxieties and worries and that you are always surrounded by love.

Choosing a loving perspective connects us to who we really are, a consciousness comprised of unlimited potential. What we say to ourselves unconsciously becomes what we consciously believe about ourselves, so let's clean up those toxic thoughts and begin a healthy conversation.

Step 3

workout exercise:

Letting go **meditation**

Time for a journal entry – reflect on the fears you identified in Step 1, use the meditation to release them

- Sitting comfortably, gently close your eyes

- Bring your awareness to the rhythm of your breath

- On each inhale, draw your awareness inwards, sink deeper into relaxation

- On each exhale, let go of any tension in your physical body

- Release any negativity which you may be experiencing

- Let go of fear, worry, anxiety

- Instead fill yourself with joy, love, peace

- Breathing in silently say to yourself: *"I am willing to let go of toxic thoughts"*
- Breathing out silently say to yourself: *"I am willing to embrace loving thoughts"*
- Breathing in silently say to yourself: *"I am willing to let go of toxic thoughts"*
- Breathing out silently say to yourself: *"I am willing to embrace loving thoughts"*
- Allow yourself to settle with each affirmation and connect with your authentic self
- When you feel ready, gently open your eyes and release the affirmations
- Namaste

Time for a journal entry – reflect on what you have let go and how you feel about your self worth now

Step 3 affirmation: "I am a divine being of love."

Step 4

COLOUR
YOUR
WELLBEING

Step 4 **goal**: Understand that you are made of energy, and that you can channel that energy

The word 'energy' is one that you can hear expressed in relation to various alternative therapies, and it can be interpreted in many different ways. But what I'm talking about isn't just a concept, or a tradition, or a way of thinking - it's something entirely tangible and entirely real.

Energy is vibration, energy is light. Our entire universe is comprised of and governed by it and - just as the atoms in our body were born in the hearts of stars - so are we. It's completely natural that our lives, our health and our well-being can be dictated by energy, but, as it's so hard to touch, people often neglect this important part of their own being.

"The next big frontier in medicine is energy medicine."
Dr Oz.

So what is this medicine called energy?

Einstein's most famous equation sums it up ($e=mc^2$) where the link between energy and physical mass is explained with uncanny elegance and clarity.

We are mass, and that mass is energy. We comprise of electrical energy, electromagnetic energy and what many people call 'subtle energy'. This latter form is what is expressed almost universally through spiritual traditions such as Buddhism, Yoga and Taoism. The nature and function of these invisible energy systems have been recognised by many healing traditions and cultures, and it's the interplay between physical energy and spiritual energy that forms the basis of so many of the things I teach my students. Every electron, every atom, every molecule, every cell, every tissue and every organ vibrates, all of which involves electrical activity.

It stands to reason that as we comprise of energy, then looking after that energy will be to the benefit of our health!

Diana says

"Instinctively, most people can feel that they are made up of energy. Learning how to guide or control it is the key to a happier, healthier life."

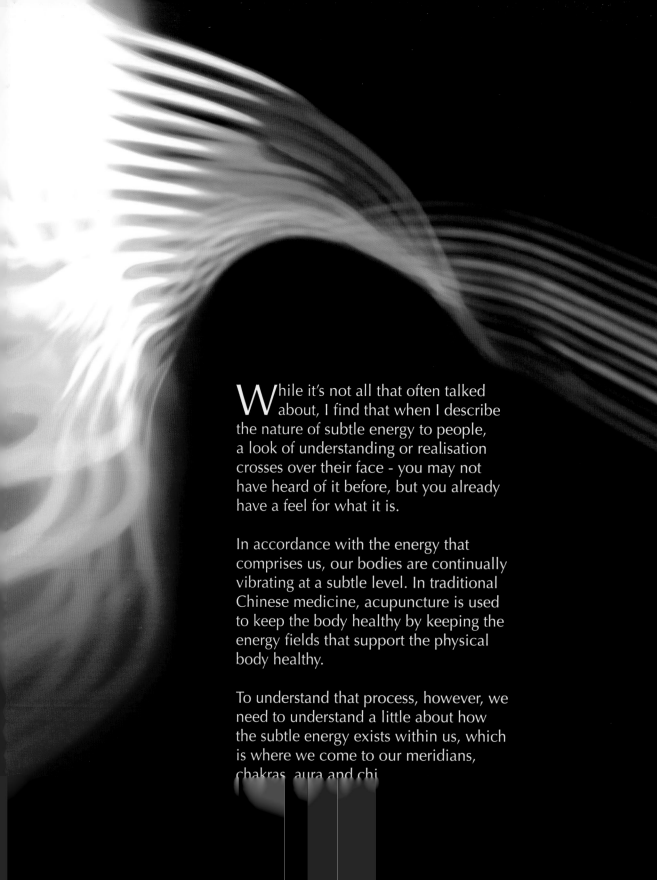

While it's not all that often talked about, I find that when I describe the nature of subtle energy to people, a look of understanding or realisation crosses over their face - you may not have heard of it before, but you already have a feel for what it is.

In accordance with the energy that comprises us, our bodies are continually vibrating at a subtle level. In traditional Chinese medicine, acupuncture is used to keep the body healthy by keeping the energy fields that support the physical body healthy.

To understand that process, however, we need to understand a little about how the subtle energy exists within us, which is where we come to our meridians, chakras, aura and chi.

The basics of subtle energy

Meridian – the energy bloodstream that flows through our body

Chakra – energy centres that are the focal point of different energy characteristics

Aura – multilayered shell of energy that surrounds every person

Chi - the subtle energy itself, our very spiritual manifestation; life itself that flows through us and gives us power from within

We have a physical body, and an exact replica in energy form.

Diana's guide to chakras

Ok then, people, time to get some clarification!

The concept of chakras, or spiritual energy points, dates back centuries, with its origins in Hindu and Buddhist spiritual tradition. As we understand them today, there are seven main chakras, each corresponding to a part of the mind, body or soul and each defined by a particular energy vibration, or colour:

Muladhara (red)
The Root Chakra represents our survival instincts and is linked to our potential for prosperity.

Anahata (green)
The Heart Chakra symbolises love, compassion, balance and influences our immune system.

Vishuddha (blue)
The Throat Chakra represents self expression, our ability to communicate and influences how we generate energy for our bodies.

Swadhisthana (orange)
The Sacral Chakra represents our relationships, physical health and influences everything from pleasure to addiction and our stress response.

Manipura (yellow)
The Solar Plexus Chakra represents our emotions and personal power, and influences our physical digestive system.

Ajna (indigo)
The Third Eye Chakra represents the balance between our visual sight and our innate intuition and influences our circadian rhythms.

Sahasrara (violet)
The Crown Chakra represents our consciousness, spiritual enlightenment and the connection between our nervous system and our physical body.

How energy effects you

The energetic and physical body link via the endocrine system, which is the biological network responsible for creating and regulating hormones. Hormones are key in regulating our body's processes, and physically these chemical messages influence the nervous system, stimulate blood circulation, and energetically release blockages to help balance chakras.

But how can this be quantified? Everything that is alive is connected and has its own Chi energy. This energy can be measured like any other electromagnetic wave, in hertz (Hz) - it's the same way we measure the vibrational frequencies of essential oils when practising aromatherapy (for example, rose essential oil vibrates at a rate of 320MHz – the highest frequency of all aromatherapy oils).

It's why aromatherapy is such a big part of the process I teach to my students - it can help to raise your own vibrational frequency and promote emotional change as well as physical wellness. If something as simple as the vibration of an essential oil can encourage spiritual growth and realisation, just imagine the power of love, purity and wholeness that can come from truly understanding the vibrational power of all forms of energy.

Energy - the next step

Ever heard of Coloured Light Therapy? It's something I practise and I have been impressed by the wonderful benefits it has on those that come to me for a helping hand.

Much like the way aromatherapy oils have their own unique vibrations, so does light. In fact, that's how light gets its various colours, from its own energy signature.

Using light alone you can: boost your immune system; oxygenate your blood and lower blood sugar; help with relaxation; calm the adrenals; improve sleep; increase blood circulation; increase vitamin D levels; restore emotional balance and raise levels of consciousness. It sounds too good to be true, but it really isn't. I've helped dozens of people with all sorts of conditions from stress to insomnia, pre-menstrual syndrome to depression, all with the help of a Monocrom Coloured Light Dome that alters your vibrations and therefore your state of consciousness. I heartily recommend you try it out for yourself!

Suffice to say, light carries information to cells much faster than e.g. neural signalling, and has a profound effect on the functioning of cells within the body.

Later in this chapter, I'll teach you how to 'breathe in the light' so that you can understand and feel these benefits for yourself.

"Studies show that the presence of Nitric Oxide brings greater elasticity to the arteries, veins and capillaries of the body enhancing blood flow promoting the growth of new blood vessels."

Dr Thomas Burke MD Phd.

Energy and attitude

I t's quite easy to imagine - each person's unique energy signature responds uniquely to everything we think, say, feel and experience. Our energetic body can become disrupted or blocked whenever we consciously - or unconsciously - accept or absorb negative thoughts, feelings or experiences.

Each thought has its own unique vibration and associated energetic charge, and you'll find that, for example, guilt has a sluggish, heavy energy vibration, whereas love has a light and fine vibration.

You can transform the lower vibration by changing your thinking and using energy medicine; simply moving from negative to positive thinking, and adjusting your intentions, changes the aura around you in drastic and beneficial ways.

Matter and energy are one in the same, they just exist at different frequencies. My very favourite quote by Christiane Northrup (in Women's Bodies, Women's Wisdom) is: "matter is the densest form of spirit, spirit is the lightest form of matter."

Understanding energy with Reiki

Reiki is a way of bringing energetic balance to a person's body, via the hands of a practitioner. As a way of healing and improving overall wellbeing, it allows the practitioner to channel spiritual energy to help break energy blockages. It balances energy pathways, which is really the key to strengthening and accelerating the body's own natural ability to heal itself.

Energy for your mind, body & soul

Step four is a meditation that brings us in tune with the vibrational energy of light. As we've discussed, every part of us is vibrating along specific energy pathways and frequencies, and our own unique vibrations understand the language of light.

I believe light is a nutrient just like any other vitamin or mineral and each separate wavelength or colour of the spectrum has its own nutritional value which resonates with our chakra system.

"For the rest of my life I want to reflect on what light is."

Albert Einstein.

Step 4

workout exercise:

Breathing in

the **light**

Time for a journal entry – by now you may have experienced subtle changes to your energy levels. Note how you feel before and after meditating

- Sitting comfortably, gently close your eyes
- Bring your awareness to the rhythm of your breath
- On each inhale, draw your awareness inwards, sink deeper into relaxation
- On each exhale, let go of any tension in your physical body
- Release any negativity which you may be experiencing
- Visualise above your head a vast ball of pure, white, radiant light

- Imagine your body being filled with this energy, and as it is merging with your energy field, your body is filled with the light
- Breathing in, silently say to yourself: *"my body is light"*
- Breathing out, silently say to yourself: *"I am a unique vibration of energy, light and colour"*
- Breathing in, silently say to yourself: *"my body is light"*
- Breathing out, silently say to yourself: *"I am a unique vibration of energy, light and colour"*
- Allow yourself to settle with each affirmation and connect with your authentic self
- When you feel ready, gently open your eyes and release the affirmations
- Namaste

Step 4 affirmation: "I am a unique vibration of energy, light and colour."

Step 5

YOU ARE UNIQUE

Step 5 goal: Find your balance

Any physicist will tell you that the world around you - the whole universe, in fact - is vibrating in billions of utterly unique ways.

If you imagine your own form in that way - your body as a combination of organs, cells, atoms and sub-atomic particles all vibrating in their own unique ways, linking up to create a vibrational pattern that is entirely yours - you'll realise just how fundamentally unique you really are.

In his book Extraordinary Healing, Art Brownstein MD states: "if you think of your body in terms of energy and function, rather than in terms of matter, structure and form, it will all make perfect sense."

It may be difficult at first to grasp this perspective, but Art is right - it allows you to understand the dynamic between the energetic and physical body.

The goal of this book is to show you what you are and what you can be, and that is the perfect balance of mind, body and soul so you can take your personal prosperity to the next step.

Matter meets energy

We have already looked at your chakra system - now we are going to look into exactly how this all links in to your physical body, a crucial part of the mind, body and soul triumvirate.

Every cell in your physical body is vibrating at a relatively low frequency and exists at a lower density, making it physical matter that can be interacted with directly.

Our subtle energy - which is itself a part of our body - vibrates at a much higher frequency, making it less easy to see directly. That's why you have to practise the exercises in this book - to bring you in tune with your energetic self.

Diana says

"The link between mind, body and soul isn't an analogy or an approximation - it's literal and direct."

The building blocks of life

Energy, in the form of negative electrons and positive protons are the building blocks of our subtle body.

One of the modern pioneers of energy medicine is Donna Eden, who has coined the phrase "chemistry follows energy" - which is to say that we all know how influential body chemistry is when it comes to our mood, our general wellness and our sense of 'get up and go'. Getting your energy in balance is vitally important - the relationship of your body's chemistry and your body's energy pours back into your whole inner experience. When energies flow well, physically you will feel the benefit.

Energy medicine includes aromatherapy - using essential oils and their unique vibrations to create balance. Such techniques promote the relationship between energy and chemistry to correct energetic and hormonal imbalances, the goal being to raise the level of your vibration and embrace the sense of love that can generate.

"Energy medicine works with life force, part of its power is the focus on the wellbeing of the entire body rather than merely on parts or symptoms. It is always available to help us feel better and function better."

Donna Eden.

Your chakras and your body

In Step 4, we looked at the relevance of your chakras in terms of your energetic self. But let's not forget that these chakras have direct relationships to your physical and emotional body. Here's a little reminder:

Muladhara (red)
The Root Chakra increases physical energy, vitality, stamina, grounding and stability.

Swadhisthana (orange)
The Sacral Chakra stimulates creativity, productivity, pleasure, optimism and enthusiasm.

Manipura (yellow)
The Solar Plexus Chakra increases fun, humour, lightness, personal power and intellect.

Anahata (green)
The Heart Chakra supports balance, harmony, love, nurturing and acceptance.

Vishuddha (blue)
The Throat Chakra increases calmness, peace, kindness, truth and honesty.

Ajna (indigo)
The Third Eye Chakra supports insight, intuition, imagination and creativity.

Sahasrara (violet)
The Crown Chakra increases inner peace, flow, stillness and consciousness.

The word 'chakra' itself directly translates as 'wheel of light', and it's well known that living tissue both emits and responds to different frequencies of light in many different ways. Just look at how plants lean towards sunlight!

Your chakra and your body

Bruce H. Lipton once said: "diseased tissue emits its own unique energy signature, which differs from the energy emitted by surrounding healthy cells." I find this an incredibly useful reminder that one needs to consider energy medicine in terms of the physical body, and well as the mind and soul. There is a keen, close relationship between hormonal balance (the endocrine system) and chakra balance, with the latter being more easily manipulated once you understand how to do so.

Remember, this chapter isn't about energy or chemistry, it's about BOTH.

The way these chakras fit together is different for everyone - we're all unique after all. Your energy centres all respond to your unique electromagnetic frequencies, which means that they also contain the individual personality and emotions of that person.

The pattern of colour and light is unique to each person, and it's safe to say that no two are alike and no pattern is ever the same.

"Energy signals are 100 times more efficient and infinitely faster than physical chemical signalling. What kind of signalling would your trillion-celled community prefer? Do the math"

Bruce H. Lipton.

The hormone connection

As well as the electrical energy that governs the activity of your atoms, cells and subtle energy, your body and brain are chemical machines. The influence of chemistry on your mood and physique are obvious - just think of the last time you took a tablet for a headache!

The way your body and brain interact chemically is controlled by hormones, which are easiest to think of as chemical messengers. They instruct your cells, tissues and organs what to do, and are themselves instructed by your body's energies.

Hormones are released in your body thanks to the endocrine glands; they dispatch the hormone messengers directly into your bloodstream and they do it with with clarity, purpose and precision in terms of their destination.

The mission of a single hormone may be to stimulate or suppress the growth, activation or inhibition of specific aspects of the immune system, or the regulation of metabolism - your body really is an incredible system!

But despite how wonderful this system is, we're still concentrating our efforts on your energy systems to get a balance of the two - it's simply a more efficient way of taking control of your own mind, body and soul.

Energy
meditation

T he fifth workout in my Mind,
Body & Soul Workout Guide
is a simple meditation that I
find to be both relaxing and
invigorating.

The key here is visualisation -
use the image on page 117 to
help you visualise your chakra
energy centres and their colours.
It might take a little practise,
but keep at it - the results are
wonderful.

Step 5

workout exercise:

Energy meditation

Time for a journal entry – can you feel the balance between your physical and energetic body?

- Sitting comfortably, gently close your eyes
- Bring your awareness to the rhythm of your breath
- On each inhale, draw your awareness inwards, sink deeper into relaxation
- On each exhale, let go of any tension in your physical body
- Breathing in, connect with the energy of your root chakra, visualise a strong vibrant red at the base of your spine, say to yourself: *"I am"*
- Breathing out, you feel physically grounded and present
- Breathing in, connect with the energy of your sacral chakra, visualise a golden energising orange around your lower back and abdomen, say to yourself: *"I nourish"*
- Breathing out, you feel physically cleansed and supported
- Breathing in, connect with the energy of your solar plexus chakra, visualise a bright yellow of the sun above your navel, say to yourself: *"I feel"*
- Breathing out, you feel physically warm and confident

- Breathing in, connect with the energy of your heart chakra, visualise a beautiful green colour moving into your heart centre, say to yourself: *"I love"*
- Breathing out, you feel physically enriched and loved
- Breathing in, connect with the energy of your throat chakra, visualise calming blues surrounding your throat, say to yourself: *"I speak"*
- Breathing out, you feel physically able to self-express and communicate freely
- Breathing in, connect with the energy of your third eye, visualise indigos filling your forehead, mentally say to yourself: *"I see"*
- Breathing out, you gain clarity and feel energised
- Breathing in, connect with the energy of your crown chakra, visualise vibrant violets showering above your head, say to yourself: *"I understand"*
- Breathing out, you feel physically and energetically connected to universal consciousness
- Allow yourself to settle with all the iridescent colours showering around you
- When you feel ready, gently open your eyes and release the affirmations
- Namaste

Step 5 affirmation: "I recognise my physical and energetic body are in balance and harmony"

Step 6

YOGA
WITH DIANA

Step 6 **goal**: Learn to **love** yoga!

The physical aspect of yoga I practice is part of a system called *Hatha* yoga - *'Ha'* in Sanskrit meaning sun and *'tha'* meaning moon - which uses *asanas* (postures) to harness *prana* (life-force energy) that circulates throughout the human body.

We will experience an ancient ritual designed to greet the sun and the moon in this week's workout exercise, which combines a balance of *asanas* and *pranayama* (breath). Each movement connects with the breath, bringing different energetic qualities to the subtle body. To me it conveys bringing both the physical and spiritual aspect of ourselves together as one.

"Yoga is the ability to direct the mind exclusively toward an object, and to sustain that direction without any distractions."

Patanjali.

My yoga philosophy

Yoga nourishes my mind, my body and my soul. It is the ultimate exercise in my guide and that's why this chapter is predominantly just exercise.

Yoga allows me to completely surrender the sense of self; the 'I' just falls away. It brings me back to that feeling of connectedness and it also helps me to become mindful of my breath and movement and to recognise just how busy my mind is.

It has supported me through some great times as well as some real challenges: times of familiarity along with times of change, including two pregnancies when my body was changing dramatically. Pracising yoga has also helped me ride waves of emotion from the depths of despair and heartache through to incredible periods of joy and happiness.

Yoga has been a consistent part of my daily life since my early 20s. The first time I experienced a class, I knew I was going to have a lifelong relationship with yoga. When I think of yoga, I tend to think of classic postures like *trikonasana* (triangle pose) or *padmasana* (lotus pose), but yoga is so much more than getting myself into some weird and wonderful shapes on the mat. For me, it's a way of life, a discipline and a commitment - a sacred place where I can explore self awareness and self acceptance.

One of yoga's most basic principles is to teach us to be here, now, in the present moment. I say 'basic', but in reality for many it's the hardest principle to master, to live simply for today. Whenever I step off the mat I come away feeling the flow, but most importantly *being* the flow.

The aim of each class I lead is to help people connect with their inner selves, their power within and their own truth - this is where the magic happens. You get strong, calm, creative, intuitive and you feel great. In my experience it has given me the confidence to move forward with my life. I know I wouldn't have achieved as many things as I have without experiencing yoga; that's why you're now reading this book!

Diana says

"The sun salutation is a great way to begin and develop your yoga practice. Try to use the breath to find balance between effort and ease."

1. Yama
Involves exploring our behaviour towards oursleves and others, and our attitudes toward our environment. Comprised of five qualities: *Ahimsa* (non-violence), *Satya* (truthfulness), *Asteya* (non-stealing), *Brahmacharya* (moderation) and *Aparigraha* (non-possessiveness).

2. Niyama
Involves self-observation and exploring our attitude toward ourselves, consisting of *Saucha* (cleanliness), *Santosa* (contentment), *Tapas* (fiery cleansing), *Svadhyaya* (self study) and *Isvara Pranidhana* (devotion).

3. Asana
The practice of postures, incorporating the breath, to bring awareness to the mind.

4. Pranayama
This is the practice of breath-control to energise and balance the body and mind, with the flow of lengthening the breath and expanding *prana*.

5. Pratyahara
Is the act of sense withdrawal to influence relaxation and internalisation of the senses to activate our mind and detach from the external world.

6. Dharana
Focuses on concentration and holding attention on one object.

7. Dhyana
Involves meditation prolonged focus of the mind on a subject.

8. Samandhi
Is the ultimate awakened state of self realisation, pure awareness and freedom.

Patanjali's Yoga Sutras and the Eight Limbs of Yoga

The more you learn to love yoga you will, as I did, eventually come across Patanjali's Yoga Sutras. They were originally written in Sanskrit, the language of yoga, and can be described as a classical guidebook of *Raja* or Royal Yoga based on Pantanjali's teachings. It's made up of 195 aphorisms (concise words of wisdom) to describe the nature and workings of the human mind, techniques to master the mind, and techniques to reach heightened levels of consciousness. As well as a path toward states of happiness, stillness and serenity, the Sutras have an exact and complex meaning that generate contemplation. Traditionally they would have been taught and memorised as a chant.

The sage's teachings are divided into four books or chapters to represent different stages of yogic development: *Samadhi-pada* (contemplation), *Sadhana-pada* (practice), *Vibhuti-pada* (accomplishments) and *Kaivalya-pada* (absoluteness).

The Sutras are just as relevant in today's modern world teaching us that we are in fact infinitely more than our mind, offering a path for achieving enlightenment through the mastery and practice of the Eight Limbs of Yoga, see left, (often referred to as *Ashtanga* Yoga - 'ashta' meaning '*eight*' and '*anga*' meaning limb, not to be confused with the popular school of *Ashtanga Vinyasa* Yoga taking its name from the eight limbs).

When you delve into the history of the Yoga Sutras you will find there are many translations offering their own unique translations of Patanjali's eight-fold path yoga system. If you are a newcomer to yoga or a dedicated practitioner, yoga philosophy can bring greater awareness of the self.

The sun and moon

Thousands of years old, *Surya Namaskar* is known as sun salutations, and is easily one of the most popular sequences of yoga there is.

By contast, *Chandra Namaskar* is a moon sequence and is traditionally done when there is a full moon. Use these sequences to find balance between your female and masculine energies.

A little tip: the inhale opens your body, the exhale closes it. It's time to connect with your breath...

Time for a journal entry - note your progress and how your strength and stamina builds

Step 6

workout exercise:

Surya Namaskar

&

Chandra Namaskar

Surya Namaskar

1 Namaste

2 Tadasana - connect with your breath

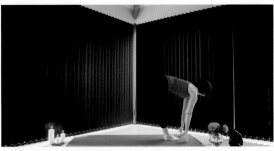

5 Ardha Uttanasana - inhale, lengthen spine,
look toward third eye centre

6 Caturanga Dandasana - exhale, jump or step back,
tuck in elbows and engage abdomen

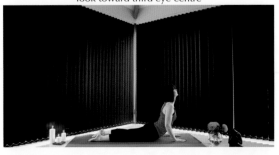

Or modify 7 with Bhujangasana

8 Ardho Muka Svanasana - exhale, hold for 5 breaths

11 Urdhva Hastasana - inhale, look towards thumbs

12 Tadasana - connect with the energy

3 Urdhva Hastasana - inhale, look towards thumbs

4 Uttanasana - exhale, fold forward from hips

Or modify 6 with Knees, Chest, Chin

7 Urdhva Muka Svanasana - inhale, lift heart centre

9 Ardha Uttanasana - inhale, jump or step forward,
lengthen spine, look toward third eye centre

10 Uttanasana - exhale, fold forward from hips

13 Namaste

Repeat 4 times. As your
strength and stamina build,
increase the number of
sequences.

Chandra Namaskar

1 Namaste

2 Urdhva Hastasana - inhale, look towards thumbs

5 Crescent Moon (right leg) - inhale, look updwards

6 Ardho Muka Svanasana - exhale, hold for 5 breaths, move through plank to 7

9 Bhujangasana - inhale, lift heart centre

10 Ardho Muka Svanasana - exhale, hold for 5 breaths

13 Uttanasana - exhale, fold forward from hips

14 Urdhva Hastasana - inhale, look towards thumbs

3 Uttanasana - exhale, fold forward from hips

4 Lunge - step left leg back

7 Knees, Chest, Chin - exhale

8 Transition - inhale

11 Lunge - step left leg forward

12 Crescent Moon (left leg) - inhale, look updwards

15 Namaste

Repeat 4 times, alternate
stepping left and right
leg back at the beginning of
each sequence

Step 7

AUTHENTIC
SELF

Step 7 **goal**:

Be **grateful** for

all you are

Do you remember what we said back in Step 1: step out of your head and live from the heart?

I hope that by now you've really started to get a handle on what that means. Throughout this guide I've tried to show practical methods that have really worked for real people, methods that involve meditation, exercises and proper nutrition in order to harmonise the body and mind and let the soul, the true loving you, flourish. That way, you can go out and get whatever you want out of life.

But I know from my own emotional transition that this isn't necessarily easy, and there are many obstacles along the way - I've found life has a habit of throwing us off course at the worst of times, but it's important not to give up. Just like with anything else in life, practise makes perfect!

So, please remember to practise all you've learned, as that will become a daily reinforcement toward a lifelong commitment. Let go of negative beliefs and surrender that ego/fear voice and let in a loving perspective. Step out of your head and live from the heart.

The power of gratitude

The true purpose of this course has been to balance and develop your mind, your body and your soul so that they can exist in alignment and you can seek the prosperity that's right for you.

You should already be feeling the benefits of the new energetic pattern you've been creating, and in this way healing your fears to appreciate that your ego, the nagging voice, will keep you in misery and search out problems for you to worry about. Personally, I practise gratitude on a daily basis. It's an incredibly important part of my guide - understanding and appreciating all that's good in your life, being grateful for how far you've come and keeping truly positive.

The voice of gratitude will keep you on the right path, and it'll help you to find forgiveness, which is the ultimate goal in letting go of negativity.

Diana says

"Happiness is an internal emotion that doesn't require outside influence."

Your authentic self in any faith

I fervently believe that no matter what your faith, this guide still holds true. In fact, many of its teachings have origins and aspects that are traceable to a variety of traditions and cultures - there is a universal acceptance that the health of the soul is at the core of our existence.

For example The Course in Miracles attempts to extend Christian teachings to enable students to achieve spiritual transformation. One of its key tenets is the idea that 'projection is perception' and I think this is an incredibly accurate and valuable way of thinking.

It simply means that what you perceive internally, you will end up perceiving externally, which is to say our perception is felt in the physical body - remember there's no separation between mind, body and soul!

Healing your past and focusing on your prosperity will make it happen. Letting go of the nagging fear voice and concentrating on your authentic self will make it happen. Being grateful for all the good things will make them happen, and help you to not give in to that negative chattering ego.

"It is the health of the soul that is the true purpose of the human experience."

Gary Zukav.

Finding your authentic self in balance

Love is a word that is used in so many places for so many reasons, but in the end it all comes down to a feeling - a wonderful, all-encompassing feeling that can overwhelm and inspire.

Balance is what this guide is all about, and prosperity is the route to finding it. Remember how I said that all goals are different, but the destination is always the same: balance.

There are a few traps that may slow you down on this journey, but there are simple ways of keeping them at bay:

Be mindful of your thoughts – suspend judgements

Have 'clean' intentions to support your energetic system, rather than polluting it with negative mindset that will lower your vibration

Holding on to resentment will not serve you in the bigger picture

Reflect on your self talk to raise awareness

Integrate these little habits into your daily routine

Begin to live the Authentic You

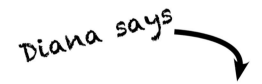

Diana says

"The authentic you is what lives underneath all the fear and self doubt, and it is beautiful and full of love."

Can you feel the balance?

Looking back at my own emotional transition, I took a leap of faith to find balance - I moved through fear to really start living my life fully.

By listening to my authentic self I was able to let go of my false beliefs, and as daunting as it was I changed my personal circumstances that prevented me from moving forward.

For me the goal was to find balance between being the best mum I could for my two boys but also having the work life I had always dreamed of. So I trusted my intuition, started my business and with each new experience I gained a renewed sense of confidence. It's been a life-changing experience that has had an incredible and positive effect on my home and family life - I have found my balance and it all started by choosing to believe in myself!

So, I think the time has come to reflect on Step 1 and realise just how far you've come over the last few weeks. That's why I suggested you keep a journal - so that after this final meditation you can look back and see the incredible progress you've made!

It's time to workout your gratitude muscles and there's no better way to do that than to repeat the prosperity meditation that we started with, but with a gratitude twist.

Step 7

workout exercise:

Gratitude **meditation**

Time for a journal entry – look back at the notes you made of your fears and goals. How do you feel about them now, and how do you feel about the balance in your life?

- Sitting comfortably, gently close your eyes
- Bring your awareness to the rhythm of your breath
- On each inhale, draw your awareness inwards, sink deeper into relaxation
- On each exhale, let go of any tension in your physical body
- Release any negativity which you may be experiencing
- Now feel your energy flowing with ease
- Breathing in, say to yourself: *"I flow in rhythm with my mind, body and soul"*

- Breathing out silently say to yourself: *"I welcome balance into all areas of my life"*
- Breathing in silently say to yourself: *"I express gratitude in all areas of my life"*
- Breathing out silently say to yourself: *"I welcome prosperity into all areas of my life"*
- Allow yourself to settle with each affirmation and connect with your authentic self
- When you feel ready, gently open your eyes and release the affirmations
- Namaste

Time for a journal entry – let the voice of your authentic self flow on the page, write from the heart, expressing the gratitude that you feel inside, and the power of love that comes with it. You can find the prosperity you seek.

Step 7 affirmation: "I choose to live with gratitude today."

Final thoughts

A PARTING WORD FROM ME

Firstly, I'd like to thank you for taking on this incredible journey with me. I sincerely hope that, over the last seven weeks, you've become more aware of yourself in every way: your mind, your body and your soul. They do say that knowledge is power, so by now you must be incredibly powerful!

Every one of the seven steps you've taken with me affects your whole life, but some people can find that, going forward, it can be difficult to remain focused on what's important.

That's why I sometimes recommend that people try to break down their life into seven discrete aspects, so that they can chose where to focus what they've learned from the Mind, Body & Soul Workout Guide.

For me the key areas for change or improvement are: relationships, personal life, health & fitness, having more fun, improving finances, a career-change or something community-based.

Simply work out what's important to you and concentrate on that - trust me, the rest will follow!

With the goal of creating prosperity and awareness through understanding the relationship between your physical body, your energy patterns, what you eat and how you exercise, and above all how you release your ego's false projections, you can achieve the ultimate goal: balance.

Some quick reminders

Be willing and commit to your prosperity mindset

Raise awareness of who you are, and be mindful

Eat real food and feed natural products to your skin

Get active and connect with your breath

Have 'clean', positive thoughts and intentions

Remember the importance of balance: everything is in relationship and is better when in alignment

Know that you are energy, and that you are able to control and channel that energy

Remember each Step's ultimate goals, and don't be afraid to dip in and out of this book whenever you feel like you might be losing a bit of focus.

And above all remember that we are all unique; we are all miracles!

Natural health and healing wishes,

Acknowledgements

This book would have not been possible without the contribution of my dream team:

I am indebted to my editor R A Farmer for his guidance and support throughout the writing of this book.

My photographer Peter Medlicott for his creativity and marketing expertise.

My extremely talented food stylist Robert Moir for his creativity and resourceful energy.

My makeup artist, the lovely Claire Evans for her guidance and professional makeup talents.

My thanks to TV producer Nicholas Ralph for developing my initial ideas and creating a fantastic title and video, which is now widely recognised as The Mind, Body and Soul Workout Guide.

I am also deeply grateful for the loving support and encouragement of my family, my boys and those closest to me, including my wonderful friends, and continued support from my clients and students.

Editor R A Farmer
author of The Deconstructing World

All photography by Peter Medlicott Photography
www.petermedlicott.com

Makeup by Claire Evans
www.claireevansmakeup.com

Video by Nick Ralph
www.videoadvert.tv

Hair by Kamigata Lifestyle Salon & Spa
www.kamigata.co.uk

Amethyst Digital Nature Phoenix Pendant by Guy & Max
www.guyandmax.com

To keep up with new tips and what's next for me, follow my blog: www.dianabrook.co.uk